**BOOSEY & HAWKES
CHORAL TREASURY**

Poston: *Balulalow*
two-part chorus & piano

UPPER VOICES

DIFFICULTY: ★★☆☆☆

Elizabeth Poston
Balulalow

for two-part chorus & piano

Text

O my deir heart, young Jesus sweet,
Prepare Thy cradle in my spreit;
And I sall rock Thee in my heart,
And never more from Thee depart.

But I sall praise Thee ever moir
With songes sweet unto Thy gloir;
The knees of my heart sall I bow,
And sing that richt Balulalow!

James, John and
Robert Wedderburn

Published by Boosey & Hawkes Music Publishers Ltd
Aldwych House
71–91 Aldwych
London
WC2B 4HN

www.boosey.com

© Copyright 1928 by Hawkes & Son (London) Ltd

ISMN 979-0-060-12847-9
ISBN 978-1-78454-046-3

This impression 2014

Printed in the EU by Halstan

Music origination by Anna Williams

BALULALOW

Words by
James, John and
Robert Wedderburn

ELIZABETH POSTON

© Copyright 1928 by Hawkes & Son (London) Ltd

19329

*Pronounce *spreet*

BOOSEY & HAWKES CHORAL TREASURY

Drawing upon our rich archive, the *Boosey & Hawkes Choral Treasury* presents a selection of exciting choral opportunities for choirs of all types and abilities wishing to explore new choral territories. A perfect resource for inspiring and accessible choral masterworks of the twentieth century and beyond, this series restores many difficult to obtain sacred and secular classics to the repertoire.

Selected choral music for upper voices from Boosey & Hawkes

Composer	Work	ISMN
Stephen Adams	*The Holy City* (SA/SSA & piano)	979-0-060-01005-7/01008-8
Gwyn Arch	*Four Negro Spirituals* (SSA & piano)	979-0-060-01039-2
Béla Bartók	*Enchanting song* (SSA a cappella)	979-0-060-01153-5
	Spring (SSA a cappella)	979-0-060-01227-3
May Brahe	*Bless this house* (SA & piano)	979-0-051-41449-9
Benjamin Britten	*Friday Afternoons* (1–4 parts & piano)	979-0-060-10500-5
	A Ceremony of Carols (SSA & harp/piano)	979-0-060-01410-9
Aaron Copland	*Old American Songs* suite I (SA & piano)	979-0-051-47699-2
	Old American Songs suite II (SA & piano)	979-0-051-47803-3
Gerald Finzi	*Let us now praise famous men* (SA & piano)	979-0-060-03035-2
	Ten children's songs (SS & piano)	979-0-060-11036-8
Michael Head	*The little road to Bethlehem* (SA & piano)	979-0-060-03241-7
	The ships of Arcady (SSA & piano)	979-0-060-03263-9
	Star Candles (SA & piano)	979-0-060-03268-4
Thomas Hewitt Jones	*All-weather friends* (two parts & piano)	979-0-060-12531-7
Herbert Howells	*Good counsel* (unison voices & piano)	979-0-060-12351-1
	Irish wren song (two parts & piano)	979-0-060-12352-8
	A New Year carol (two parts & piano)	979-0-060-12353-5
	Piping down the valleys wild (two parts & piano)	979-0-060-12354-2
John Ireland	*Ex ore innocentium* (SS & piano)	979-0-060-03371-1
Zoltán Kodály	*Evening song* (SSA a cappella)	979-0-060-03515-9
	Hippity-hoppity (SSA a cappella)	979-0-060-03529-6
	Mountain nights (SSSSA a cappella)	979-0-060-03577-7
James MacMillan	*New-made for a king* (SSAA & piano)	979-0-060-12578-2
	Nova! Nova! Ave fit ex Eva (SSA a cappella)	979-0-060-12637-6
Bohuslav Martinů	*Three sacred songs* (SSA & violin)	979-0-060-03697-2
Peter Maxwell Davies	*Five carols* (SSA a cappella)	979-0-060-03749-8
Joseph Phibbs	*Gaudeamus omnes* (SSA a cappella)	979-0-060-12813-4
Elizabeth Poston	*Balulalow* (two parts & piano)	979-0-060-12847-9
	Dance to your daddie (SA & piano)	979-0-060-02032-2
Roger Quilter	*Non nobis Domine* (unison/SSA & piano)	979-0-060-02180-0/02179-4
Will Todd	*The Lord is my Shepherd* (SSA & piano)	979-0-060-12935-3
	This other world (SSA & piano)	979-0-060-12446-4
Ralph Vaughan Williams	*Linden Lea* (unis/SS/SSA & piano)	979-0-060-08972-5/02849-6/02848-9

POSTON: BALULALOW – two-part chorus & piano

ISBN 978-1-78454-046-3

BOOSEY & HAWKES

AN IMAGEM COMPANY

ISMN 979-0-060-12847-9